Discovery KIDS™

So Gross!

LIVE. LEARN. DISCOVER.

PaRragon

Bath · New York · Singapore · Hong Kong · Cologne · Delhi · Melbourne

First published by Parragon in 2009

Parragon
Queen Street House
4 Queen Street
Bath BA1 1HE, UK

ISBN 978-1-4075-7885-9

Printed in China

Contents!

Fleshy Facts

Cut marks in the skull of the oldest human skull ever found point to a grisly secret. Work through the maze to find it out. When you find the exit route, it will lead you to the correct answer!

Discovery Fact

The oldest human skull ever found is 160,000 years old.

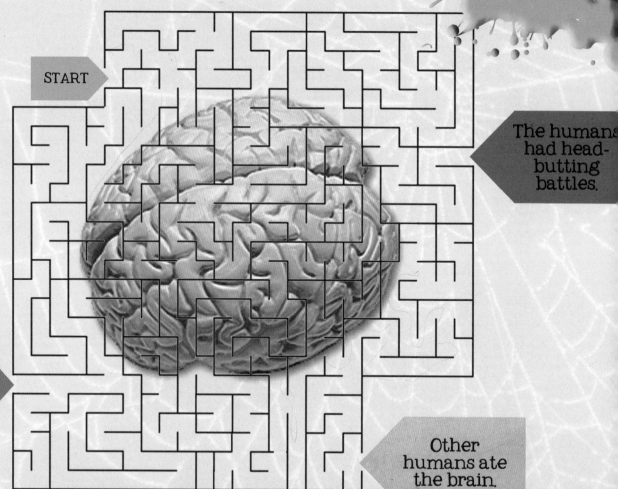

START

The humans had head-butting battles.

Maggots ate into the brains of living humans.

Other humans ate the brain.

4

Pirate Punishment

Pirates roamed the seas in the 1700s, seizing ships and stealing treasure! But if they were caught, they were given a horrible punishment. Crack the code to find out what it was!

z	y	x	w	v	u	t	s	r	q	p	o	n	m	l	k	j	i	h	g	f	e	d	c	b	a
a	b	c	d	e	f	g	h	i	j	k	l	m	n	o	p	q	r	s	t	u	v	w	x	y	z

k	r	i	z	g	v	h		d	v	i	v		s	z	m	t	v	w		g	s	v	m

o	v	u	g		g	l		i	l	g		r	m		z		x	z	t	v		u	l	i

z	o	o		g	l		h	v	v

Discovery Fact™

Pirate flags were flown as a warning. The message was "Surrender or die!"

Answer: Pirates were hanged, then left to rot in a cage for all to see.

Ahoy There!

Below is a list of four of the meanest pirate captains ever—but only the first letters of their names are shown. Find their complete names in the word puzzle to finish the list.

E_ _ _ _ _ _ L_ _

Is said to have once cut off and cooked a man's lips.

H_ _ _ _ M_ _ _ _ _ _

Accidentally blew up his own ship during a party, killing 350 men but escaping himself.

B_ _ _ _ _ _ _ _ _ _

Went into battle with burning fuses tied in his hair to make him look devilish. He drank rum mixed with gunpowder.

W_ _ _ _ _ _ K_ _ _

After he was caught, his corpse was left hanging in a cage to rot for over 20 years.

```
Y  Y  G  J  W  V  H  D  D  L  F
K  M  J  Y  W  J  A  Y  C  Y  O
W  K  C  U  A  U  P  B  Z  A  N
N  A  G  R  O  M  Y  R  N  E  H
W  I  L  L  I  A  M  K  I  D  D
F  Q  V  E  U  T  P  N  B  G  F
K  M  R  F  J  V  M  W  A  J  F
K  S  C  E  W  G  T  X  Z  W  E
E  D  W  A  R  D  L  O  W  C  R
D  R  A  E  B  K  C  A  L  B  B
S  D  P  G  C  M  M  T  Y  E  Q
```

Royal Nutcases!

Through the centuries, many kings and queens have been mad, bad, or plain disgusting. Follow the lines to match these crazy royals with their crazier behavior.

No wonder Louis XIV of France had only three baths ever. In his 2,000-room palace at Versailles near Paris, there were no bathrooms.

A. BRITISH KING GEORGE THE THIRD

B. DUKE GIAN GASTONE OF TUSCANY

C. KING NABONIDUS OF BABYLON

D. IVAN THE TERRIBLE OF RUSSIA

1. Thought he was a tree.

2. Stayed in a stinking bed for seven years.

3. Thought he was a goat.

4. Nailed a hat onto someone's head.

i. (His other behavior is too awful to mention.)

ii. (He insisted on grazing in a field.)

iii. (He was driven mad by the pain of illness.)

iv. (He refused to get up ever again.)

Rotten Romans!

Ancient Romans had some of the most disgusting habits ever. And they had a gross way of gazing into the future. Find three gruesome animal parts in the word puzzle below to discover what they examined to make their predictions.

CLUE:
One of the body parts is from a sheep, one from an ox, and one from a hen.

```
S D S A N Z S A T E
H H T H P J T N M S
E J U E N T U I E S
E U G N J K G M Q G
P U L S J D L A O N
S T A L W Q A L N U
G J M I N E M G F L
U W I V B P I U T S
T A N E E M N T J X
X C A R M G A S Y O
```

Discovery Fact™

A favorite sport in ancient Rome was to watch gladiators fight to the death!

Answer: Sheep's gut, ox's lungs, hen's liver

Doctor, Doctor!

Discovery Fact™

The "humors" were the substances that doctors believed made up the body.

Medieval doctors believed disease was linked to the four "humors." If a person's humors were out of balance, they would become ill. Read around the word circles to find out what the four humors were! The first letter of each word is the letter in the center of the circle.

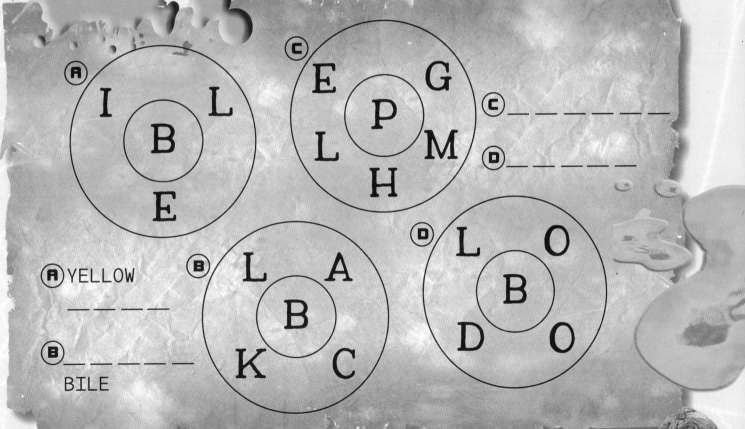

Ⓐ YELLOW
_ _ _ _ _

Ⓑ _ _ _ _ _ _
BILE

Ⓒ _ _ _ _ _ _ _ _

Ⓓ _ _ _ _ _ _

Answer: A. Yellow bile, B. black bile (bile is stomach juices), C. phlegm (snot), D. blood

Crazy Cures!

Below are some sickening medical prescriptions from history. Follow the lines to match each illness to its cure.

A. Baldness in ancient Egypt

B. A Roman stomachache

C. A medieval fever

D. A medieval fit

1. SNiFF CRUMBS OF ROASTED CUCKOO UP YOUR NOSE.

2. EAT A SPIDER WRAPPED iN A RAISIN.

3. RUB CROCODILE FAT AND LETTUCE LEAVES ON YOUR HEAD.

4. GARGLE WITH MUSTARD.

Answer: A.3, B.4, C.2, D.1

Poor Kids!

It wasn't easy being a kid in the 1800s—you were given the worst jobs! Crack the code below to find out the most disgusting way to make money!

z	y	x	w	v	u	t	s	r	q	p	o	n	m	l	k	j	i	h	g	f	e	d	c	b	a
a	b	c	d	e	f	g	h	i	j	k	l	m	n	o	p	q	r	s	t	u	v	w	x	y	z

x	l	o	o	v	x	g	r	m	t		w	l	t		z	m	w		x	z	g

k	l	l	k		u	i	l	n		g	s	v		t	i	l	f	m	w		d	s	r	x	s

d	z	h		f	h	v	w		g	l		n	z	p	v

o	v	z	g	s	v	i

Discovery Fact™

Until recently, teachers were allowed to beat a child in school if they were being bad or lazy.

Answer: Collecting dog and cat poop from the ground, which was used in making leather.

11

King of the Castle!

There were no flush toilets in medieval castles. Instead, lords and ladies sat over chutes in the wall! Who had to pick up the poop? Work through the maze to find it out. When you find the exit route, it will lead you to the correct answer!

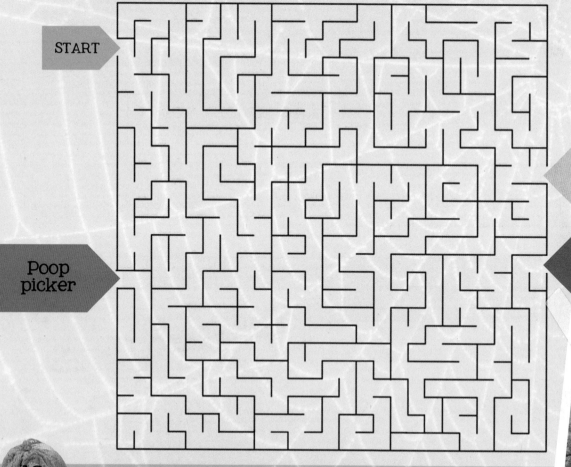

START

Gong farmer

Poop picker

Stinky fingers

12

Answer: Gong farmer

Joust!

Jousting was a popular sport in medieval times, but, despite wearing armor, knights were often injured. But which of these ways of getting injured are true, and which are false?

A. TRUE or FALSE?
Crushed under a wooden spectator stand as it collapsed.

B. TRUE or FALSE?
Dragged under the hooves of a horse after falling off.

C. TRUE or FALSE?
Falling onto the sharp point of the jousting lance.

Answer: A True, B True, C False (the points of the lances weren't sharp)

13

Freaky Fashion!

Women (and men!) in history have certainly suffered for their fashions. Read around the word circles to discover some terrible fashion choices! The first letter of each word is the letter in the center of the circle.

A

A type of overshoe worn during the 1700s to keep shoes off the dirty streets.

_ _ _ _ _ _ _ _

B

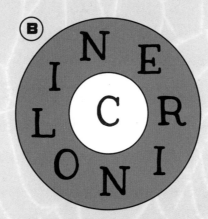

This skirt was so big, that sometimes women could barely get through the doorway!

_ _ _ _ _ _ _ _ _

C

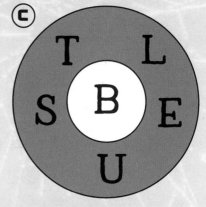

Women wore this to make their backsides appear larger!

_ _ _ _ _ _

(This freaky fashion is pictured above.)

14

Who Ate All the Pies?

Emperors were history's biggest pigs. Holy Roman Emperor Charles V (1516–1558) once ate a whole what for breakfast at 5 a.m.? Work your way through the maze to find out. When you find the exit route, it will lead you to the correct answer.

START

Fish

Cow

Chicken

Answer: Chicken

15

Magic Mice!

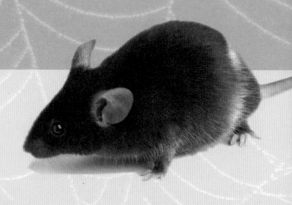

For years, wacky scientists have been experimenting with DNA (the genetic instructions found in all living things). What crazy thing happened when they mixed cells from a glowing jellyfish with mouse cells? Crack the code below to find out!

z	y	x	w	v	u	t	s	r	q	p	o	n	m	l	k	j	i	h	g	f	e	d	c	b	a
a	b	c	d	e	f	g	h	i	j	k	l	m	n	o	p	q	r	s	t	u	v	w	x	y	z

q	v	o	o	b	u	r	h	s			n	l	f	h	v			t	i	v	v	m
								+							=							

t	o	l	d		r	m		g	s	v		w	z	i	p		n	l	f	h	v
					-			-				-									

Answer: jellyfish + mouse = green glow-in-the-dark mouse.

Discovery Fact™

Scientists at the University of Washington get elephant poop in the mail to analyze!

Feline Funny!

So, you think cats are cute? Do you know what they eat to make themselves vomit? Pick out the correct answer from below:

Cats also vomit fur balls when they've licked too much cat hair.

Animals..aaargh!

(A) **worms**

(B) **grass**

(C) **cheese**

(D) **mice**

Disgusting Dogs!

Discovery Fact™

Dogs have such a good sense of smell they can even smell human fingerprints.

If you're not a cat fan, then you must think dogs are lovable, right? Wrong! Guess what they like to roll in? Check your guess below.

(A)

moldy food

(B)

maggots

Here is a breed of dog called a Shih-poo, a cross between a Shih-tzu and a poodle. Cute dog, terrible name!

(C)

cat pee

(D)

animal poop

18

Answer: D. Animal poop

Cow Danger!

Unscramble the letters below to find out why cows are a threat to our planet!

e y t h

_ _ _ _

r f t a a

_ _ _ _ _

e u e n r h o g s e

_ _ _ _ _ _ _ _ _

a s g

_ _ _

Discovery Fact™

Cows have a four-chambered stomach that helps them break down the plants they eat.

Answer: They fart a greenhouse gas (a gas called methane).

Perfect Poop!

We all know cow manure is smelly and yucky, but it also has some very good uses! Unscramble the letters below to see what can be made with cow manure!

CLUE:
Beverage bottles are made from this.

A. TILASPC

– – – – – – –

B. EZEANIFRET

– – – – – – – – – –

CLUE:
Helps your car start in the cold.

Answer: A. Plastic, B. Antifreeze

Barnyard Crazies!

Check out this list of crazy animal behavior. Which of these gross facts are true and which are false?

There are 80 different sheep diseases, including nasal bots, blue tongue, lamb fungus, sheep measles, watery mouth, and pizzle rot.

Ⓐ Male goats pee on themselves to attract female goats.

Ⓑ Horses sometimes eat each other's poop.

Ⓒ Cows often stick their tongues up their own noses, probably to get salt and to keep flies away.

Ⓓ A sheep can look behind itself without turning its head.

Ⓔ Pigs don't sweat, so they roll in mud to stay cool.

Discovery Fact™

Farm animals live in herds and behave like an animal gang. The gang leaders bully the rest!

Answer: D is false, all the rest are true!

Killer Lizard!

The biggest lizard in the world has spit full of really bad bacteria. After it bites its prey, the victim suffers a slow, painful death as the bacteria seeps into the blood, causing blood poisoning. What is this killer lizard called? Unscramble the letters to find out.

These giant lizards grow up to 10 feet long!

DOMOOK GRADNO

___ ___ ___ ___ ___ ___ ___

___ ___ ___ ___ ___ ___

CLUE:
It's named after a mythical creature and an Indonesian island.

22

Answer: Komodo dragon

Seriously Creepy Crawlers!

The three word squares below contain the names of some of the world's meanest creepy crawlers. Read clockwise around each square, starting from any letter, to discover the names!

Animals.. Aaaargh!

Found in tropical parts of the world. Impales prey, such as caterpillars, on its spiky legs, before eating them.

Found in parts of Europe. Sucks up worms like spaghetti.

A type of poisonous spider found worldwide. The female likes to eat the male after they have mated.

```
S P R A Y
S       I
I       N
T       G
N A M G
```

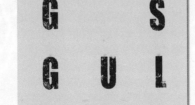

```
H O S T
G       S
G U L
```

```
W B L A
O       C
D I W K
```

Ⓐ _ _ _ _ _ _ _ _
   _ _ _ _ _

Ⓑ _ _ _ _ _
   _ _ _ _

Ⓒ _ _ _ _ _
   _ _ _ _ _

Bear Banquet!

Black bears, grizzly bears, and polar bears have been known to attack people.

Occasionally, bears will picnic on people. But which type of bear is the most vicious? Work out which bear appears most often in the word puzzle below to get the answer!

```
R P O L A R B E A R L
G O D C W K J T V R W
R W Y I C Y R S Q A R
A H S K Z W A S F E A
E C H J E C E V T B E
B P O L A R B E A R B
K P V T T D K C U A R
C W N Q Y U C E G L A
A B G Q M W A F Z O L
L G A U V K L V N P O
B R G I P S B X G N P
```

24

Snap Happy!

Crocodiles and alligators will both take a bite out of a human if they're hungry. They will often spin their prey around and around to kill it. What is this sometimes called?
Crack the code to find out.

In Florida, there are more and more homes, and fewer wild places for alligators—so alligators sometimes wander into houses and yards.

___   ___   ___   ___   ___   ___   ___   ___   ___

a	b	c	d	e	f	g	h	i	j	k	l	m	n

o	p	q	r	s	t	u	v	w	x	y	z

Discovery Fact™

Crocodiles and alligators usually hunt at night.

Animals...Aaaargh!

Scary Sharks!

Everyone is afraid of these monsters! Where do most shark attacks happen in the world? Work through the maze to find the country. When you find the exit route, it will lead you to the correct answer!

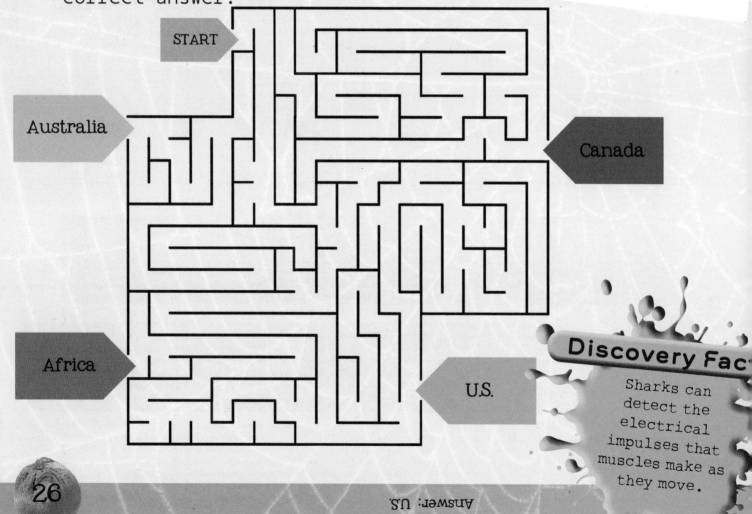

START

Australia

Canada

Africa

U.S.

Answer: U.S.

Stinkiest Stink!

Skunks can spray out a stinky fluid from scent glands around their backsides. Work through the maze to find out how far a skunk can spray! When you find the exit route, it will lead you to the correct answer!

Skunks are found in North America and South America.

Animals.. Aaaargh!

Over 16 feet

Over 23 feet

Over 6 feet

START

Answer: Over 16 feet

Protection!

Some animals have the weirdest and most disgusting ways of protecting themselves. Read these weird defense strategies, then read around the word circles to uncover which crazy creatures they belong to. The first letter of each word is the letter in the center of the circle.

A

C T O P U S O

Sends out a cloud of black ink to confuse its enemies. It keeps the ink in a special sac in its body.

A _ _ _ _ _ _ _

B

D O R N E D R A Z I L H

Tries to confuse an attacker by spouting blood from its eyes, up to a distance of 3 feet away.

B _ _ _ _ _ _
_ _ _ _ _ _

C

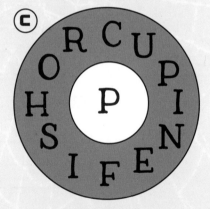

O R C U P H S I F E N I P

Can blow itself up to look like a big spiky basket ball.

C _ _ _ _ _ _ _ _ _
_ _ _ _ _

Answer: A. Octopus, B. Horned lizard, C. Porcupine fish

Small, But Deadly!

The most poisonous vertebrate in the world has enough deadly venom in it to kill ten people. Unscramble the words to find out the name of this animal!

Animals...aaargh!

HET DELONG

_ _ _ _ _ _ _ _ _

SONIPO GORF

_ _ _ _ _ _ _ _ _

Answer: The Golden poison frog

So Gross!

Discovery Fact™

Small children are most likely to catch parasitic worms because they play in soil and eat it.

There can be thousands of parasitic worm eggs in one handful of soil. Guess whether these gross worm facts are true or false!

A. TRUE or FALSE?
A tapeworm can live in a human for up to 30 years.

B. TRUE or FALSE?
Flukes are parasitic worms live in mammals and birds. Humans may get them by swimming in dirty water or eating snails.

C. TRUE or FALSE?
Almost all living creatures have parasites living on or in them. Most are harmless.

Answer: They are all true!

Not So Cute!

All babies are cute, right? Wrong! The gray nurse shark mother hatches her eggs inside her. The first babies to be born aren't as sweet as you'd expect. Crack the code below to find out why!

Animals_Aaaargh!

z	y	x	w	v	u	t	s	r	q	p	o	n	m	l	k	j	i	h	g	f	e	d	c	b	a
a	b	c	d	e	f	g	h	i	j	k	l	m	n	o	p	q	r	s	t	u	v	w	x	y	z

g	s	v	b		v	z	g		g	s	v	r	i		y	i	l	g	s	v	i	h

z	m	w		h	r	h	g	v	i	h

Discovery Fact™

The gray nurse shark gives birth to live babies called pups.

Rancid Rain Forest!

Which is the world's biggest rain forest? Unscramble the letters to find out.

ZANOAMIA

_ _ _ _ _ _ _ _

Discovery Fact™

Although it is very warm in the rain forest, it still rains every day!

32

Answer: Amazonia

Amazonian Anaconda!

The world's biggest snake is the anaconda. How long is it? Work your way through the maze to find out! When you find the right exit route, it will lead you to the correct answer!

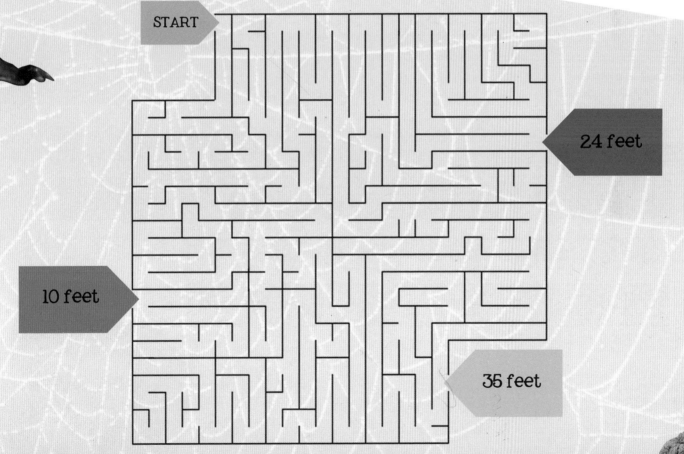

START

24 feet

10 feet

35 feet

Fishy!

Piranha fish attack in schools. Their sharp teeth can rip flesh off their victims in minutes. Can you guess what the Amazonian Indians make with piranha fish bones? Crack the code to find out!

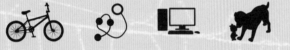   

___ ___ ___ ___   ___ ___ ___ ___ ___

a	b	c	d	e	f	g	h	i	j	k	l	m	n

o	p	q	r	s	t	u	v	w	x	y	z

34

Answer: Hair combs

In the Middle of Nowhere!

Often people in a desert will be tricked by light shimmering on the sand, mistaking it for a pool of water. What is this phenomenon known as? Unscramble the letters to find out.

RAMGIE

Discovery Fact™

A poisonous biting lizard, the Gila monster, lives in the Mexican desert.

Answer: Mirage

Stinky Beach!

What is it that can make beaches so smelly? It could be either seaweed trapped beneath the sand, or dead, rotting crabs. Search the grid below for SEAWEED and CRABS. Whichever word comes up the most is the answer!

```
R S E A W E E D E D A R L
G E D C W K C R A B S S
R A Y I C Y R S Q A R
A W S K Z W A E F E C
E E H J E C E A T B R
B E O L A R B W A R A
K D V T T D K E U A B
C W S E A W E E D L S
A B G Q M W A D Z O L
L C R A B S L V N P O
B R G I P S B X G N P
```

Discovery Fact™

Don't swim in the sea after heavy rain—that's when sewage and industrial waste get washed into it.

Arctic Flashlight!

The Arctic and Antarctic are in continual darkness for part of every year because of the way Earth tilts as it orbits the Sun. Guess how many months a year they are in darkness.

6 months ☐

4 months ☐

2 months ☐

Trash River!

The world's most disgusting river is the Citarum in Indonesia. It is choked with garbage, sewage, and industrial waste. Nine million people live along its banks. But how many factories pump waste out into it? Do the math below to find out.

$$150 \times 2 + 50 \times 4 = \boxed{}$$

Answer: $\boxed{}$ factories

Answer: 500 factories.

Lost Lake!

Some lakes are so full of chemicals that the water would burn your skin if you swam in it! One of the most polluted lakes in the world is in New York State. Crack the code to learn the name of the lake.

_ _ _ _ _ _ _ _ _

_ _ _ _

a	b	c	d	e	f	g	h	i	j	k	l	m	n

o	p	q	r	s	t	u	v	w	x	y	z

Discovery Fact™

Some lakes are so polluted that swimming and fishing are banned.

Killer Oceans!

Some parts of the oceans are so polluted there is almost no oxygen, and nothing can live there. What do we call these parts? Crack the code to find out.

_____ _____

a	b	c	d	e	f	g	h	i	j	k	l	m	n

o	p	q	r	s	t	u	v	w	x	y	z

Answer: Dead zones

Discovery Fact™

There are almost 150 areas in the world's oceans where nothing can survive.

Sick Cities!

Urumqi is said to be the most polluted city in the world. What country do you think it is in? Work through the maze to find out. When you find the exit route, it will lead you to the correct answer!

In Ranipet, India, the polluted river water is so toxic that it stings if it touches the skin.

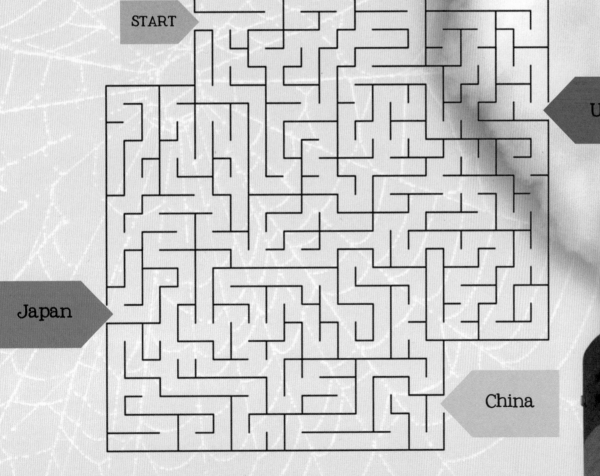

START

U.S.A.

Japan

China

Wicked World

Answer: China

Ocean Soup!

The Pacific Ocean between Hawaii and Japan is home to a vast soup of garbage that's been washed into the ocean and then trapped together in a big mass by whirling currents. What is this part of the ocean also known as? Read clockwise around the squares, starting from any letter, to find out.

A R B
G A
E G
(ARBAGE)

Discovery Fact™

Garbage dumped off the American coast can end up thousands of miles away.

Shoved on the Shore!

In 2009, the Ocean Conservancy organization arranged a one-day beach cleanup in 104 countries around the world. How many tons of garbage do you think volunteers picked up in just one day? Solve the numbers below to find out!

$$1{,}000 + 800 + 1{,}600 = \boxed{}$$

Answer: nearly  tons

It's Not Sewage!

The good news is that the creamy colored sea scum you might see washed up on a beach is not sewage. It is caused by harmless little organisms that live in the water. Unscramble the letters to discover their name!

GLAAE

____ ____ ____ ____ ____

Garbage Dump!

Discovery Fact™

In the world's poorest cities, people live in dumps, surviving off other people's garbage.

Garbage that's left lying around in cities is a big problem. The Indian city of Mumbai has come up with an unusual method to get rid of the awful smell of its 300-acre garbage dump. Crack the code to find out what it is!

z	y	x	w	v	u	t	s	r	q	p	o	n	m	l	k	j	i	h	g	f	e	d	c	b	a
a	b	c	d	e	f	g	h	i	j	k	l	m	n	o	p	q	r	s	t	u	v	w	x	y	z

k	l	f	i	r	m	t		g	s	l	f	h	z	m	w	h		l	u		j	f	z	i	g	h

l	u		k	v	i	u	f	n	v	w		w	v	l	w	l	i	z	m	g		l	m		r	g

Answer: Pouring thousands of quarts of perfumed deodorant on it.

Terrible Traffic!

The city of São Paulo in Brazil has the world's worst traffic jams—they are unbelievably long! Solve the numbers below to learn how far they can reach!

$$77 + 23 + 26 - 6 = \boxed{}$$

Answer: $\boxed{}$ miles

Wicked World

Answer: 120 miles.

Let Me Out of Here!

Here are the most crowded cities in the world, with the most number of people jammed in to each square mile. Follow the lines to match each city with its population.

A. Lagos, Nigeria

B. Cairo, Egypt

C. Manila, Philippines

1. 106,226 PEOPLE PER SQUARE MILE

2. 51,800 PEOPLE PER SQUARE MILE

3. 94,840 PEOPLE PER SQUARE MILE

Answer: A 2, B3, C1.

Mad Parties!

There are some wacky people in the world, and even wackier parties. Follow the lines to match up these parties with their national partygoers!

A. THORRABLOT MIDWINTER FEAST A buffet of seal flippers and rotting shark meat

1. MALI

2. ICELAND

B. FESTIVAL OF HOLI Paint throwing

3. INDIA

C. TOMATO FESTIVAL Throwing tomatoes

4. SPAIN

D. MUD-PLASTERING FESTIVAL Everyone slaps mud on the local buildings and on themselves

Wicked World

Answer: A2, B3, C4, D1

Full of Fog!

Smog is polluted fog that envelops industrial cities. It can be deadly poisonous.

London, England, was once so polluted with coal smoke that a poisonous yellow "smog" often enveloped the city. What was this fog nicknamed? When you find the exit route, it will lead you to the correct answer!

Potato peel

START

Lemon juice

Pea souper

48

Good Scent!

One animal has such a good sense of smell it can detect your body odor if it stands downwind of you. Is it a deer or a bear? Search the word puzzle below for DEER and BEAR. Whichever word comes up the most is the answer.

```
W  Z  B  X  K  L  B  W  Z  J  A
R  Z  S  E  D  P  X  S  F  Q  U
A  D  X  E  A  D  R  Z  R  O  B
E  X  E  H  V  R  O  S  X  A  Q
B  R  S  I  R  E  E  D  D  V  Q
G  W  K  G  U  R  W  E  Q  F  V
K  E  G  D  R  A  E  B  D  P  R
R  A  E  B  E  R  K  E  S  W  L
T  D  J  P  X  E  M  Q  D  C  L
J  N  U  W  O  R  R  W  K  I  Q
O  Y  W  L  D  O  Q  C  A  N  N
```

Wicked World

Answer: Deer

49

It Rains, It Pours!

In the wettest place in the world, it rains for 350 days of the year. Unscramble the word circles to find out where this is! The first letter of each word is the letter in the center of the circle.

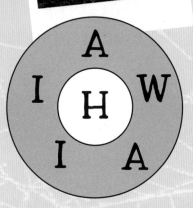

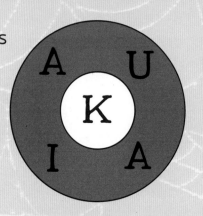

_ _ _ _ _ _ , _ _ _ _ _ _

Freezing Cold!

The Arctic and Antarctic are the coldest places on Earth. Mostly frozen, they are home to howling winds and snowstorms. Which is in the south, and which is in the north? Follow the lines to find out.

North

Antarctic

Arctic

South

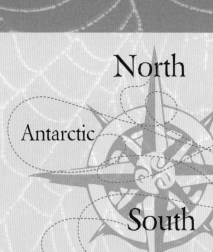

50

Dry As a Bone!

less than 80 feet ☐

less than 10 inches ☐

less than 1 inch ☐

Some deserts are so dry you can die from dehydration waiting for it to rain. Can you guess the average annual rainfall in the desert?

Marvelous Mud!

OBG ENORSKLING

_ _ _ _ _ _ _ _ _ _ _

NHAHMPCIOSIP

_ _ _ _ _ _ _ _ _ _ _

A competition held in Wales, U.K., each August involves people wading through deep puddles of mud wearing a snorkel. Unscramble the letters to find the name of the competition.

Frosty Frostbite!

Frostbite sets in when the temperature is so cold that skin freezes within a minute. First the flesh turns white, then it turns black and blistered. Eventually, it may rot and need to be cut off. Certain parts of the body are more at risk. Read clockwise around the squares, starting from any letter, to find out.

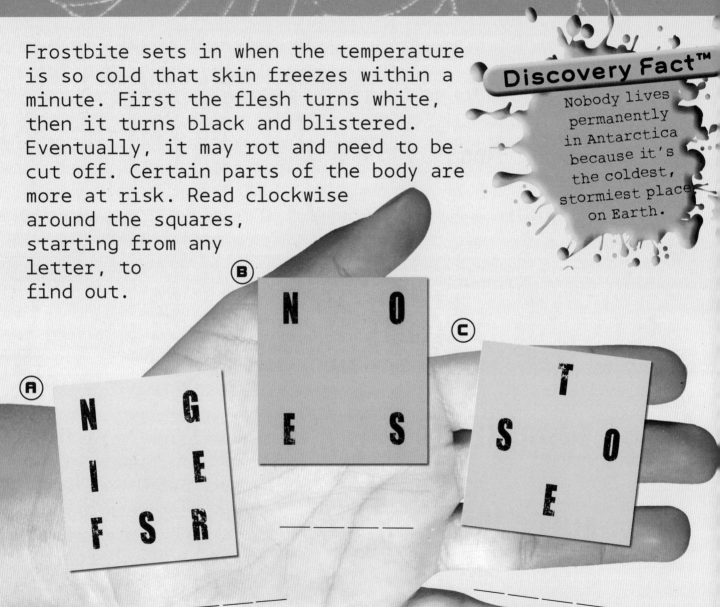

52

Clean Extremes!

To keep the environment in good condition, everyone who visits Antarctica must take home their trash. What disgusting stuff does this include? Crack the code to find the answer!

z	y	x	w	v	u	t	s	r	q	p	o	n	m	l	k	j	i	h	g	f	e	d	c	b	a
a	b	c	d	e	f	g	h	i	j	k	l	m	n	o	p	q	r	s	t	u	v	w	x	y	z

k	v	v		z	m	w		k	l	l	k

Arctic Animals!

The poles might be empty places, but there are other critters braving the ice, and they're out to get you. Follow the lines to find out about each animal.

A. Polar bear

B. Leopard seal

C. Lion's mane jellyfish

1.

These Antarctic snappers have nasty sharp teeth and a bad temper. They often attack inflatable boats and will occasionally try to bite divers or people standing on ice near the sea.

2.

This big ball of jiggling jelly has poisonous stinging tentacles that can trail out by an incredible 118 feet.

3.

These Arctic bad guys have great smell, claws as sharp as a tiger's, and can run fast. They grow over 10 feet tall, and like humans for dinner.

Answer: A3, B1, C2

Mountain Madness!

The slopes of the world's most popular mountain climbs are littered with trash left behind by climbers. The highest mountain, Everest, is strewn with a lot of different forms of garbage. Unscramble the letters to discover the most common.

Mont Blanc, in the European Alps, even had an old washing machine dumped on its slopes by a litterbug.

a. sorep

_____

b. namhu oppo

_____ _____

c. yegnox lettsob

_____ _____

Answer: A. Ropes, B. Human poop, C. Oxygen bottles

Deathly Heights!

Many climbers have died on Everest, and bodies have been left to freeze on the mountain's north face, because it is too hard to carry them down. Other mountaineers see them as they pass by. Solve the numbers below to find the grisly truth of how many frozen bodies are up there.

HE CLIMBED TOO HIGH...

$$20 \times 3 - 17 + 3 = \boxed{}$$

Answer: $\boxed{}$ bodies

Discovery Fact

Air pressure falls the higher you climb and can cause deadly changes in your body.

56

Answer: 40 bodies.

Call Crazy!

When was the first ever cell-phone call made from the top of Everest? Work through the maze to find out. When you find the exit route, it will lead you to the correct answer!

2008

2003

2007

START

Wicked World

Smelly Everest!

Everest mountaineers can be smelly because local mountain guides believe the best way to ward off altitude sickness is to eat a lot of a particularly smelly food. Search the word puzzle below for GARLIC and EGGS. Whichever word comes up the most is the answer!

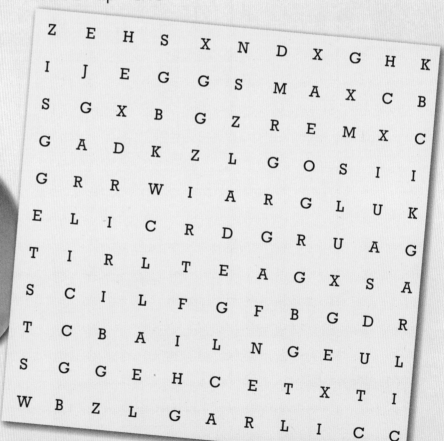

```
Z E H S X N D X G H K
I J E G G S M A X C B
S G X B G Z R E M X C
G A D K Z L G O S I I
G R R W I A R G L U K
E L I C R D G R U A G
T I R L T E A G X S A
S C I L F G F B G D R
T C B A I L N G E U L
S G G E H C E T X T I
W B Z L G A R L I C C
```

Answer: Garlic

Bad Bears!

In one place in Canada, you might see a polar bear at your kitchen window waiting for a bite of your dinner! Crack the code to find the name of the town.

__ __ __ __ __ __ __ __ __

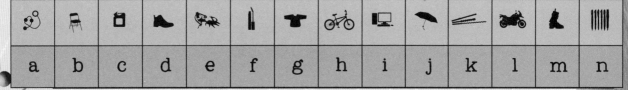

a	b	c	d	e	f	g	h	i	j	k	l	m	n

o	p	q	r	s	t	u	v	w	x	y	z

Space Vomit!

Do you think car sickness is bad? Well, traveling in space is no joke either. Read about the space illnesses below and then solve the word squares to discover the symptoms! Read clockwise around each square, starting from any letter, to find the answers.

Space toilets have bars like rollercoaster chairs to stop the astronauts from floating away as they do their space business.

Weightlessness causes astronauts to float around, not knowing which way is up.

Lack of gravity makes liquids move up, giving astronauts a head cold.

As fluids move up, astronauts feel as though they need to go to the toilet all the time.

Ⓐ

V O M
G   I
N   I   T

Ⓑ

N O T S
S   P
E C A

Ⓒ

E   I N
E   G
P

_ _ _ _ _ _ _

_ _ _ _ _ _ _ _ _ _

_ _ _ _ _ _ _

60

Stinky Gas Balls!

If you travel to outer space and visit other planets, you might be greeted by some stinky surroundings. Four planets are made from smelly gases, such as ammonia and methane—the same gases that make sewage stinky. Can you find the names of the four planets to avoid in the word puzzle below?

F	T	R	K	K	B	N	I	P	W	J
T	J	N	G	Z	Y	A	H	Z	Z	R
K	W	E	U	V	L	J	C	S	Z	A
X	T	P	R	W	Y	U	S	M	L	F
P	I	T	E	Y	U	R	A	N	U	S
W	N	U	T	M	U	Q	T	C	Q	A
J	S	N	I	S	U	M	U	U	T	H
J	V	E	P	K	L	E	R	O	A	N
K	E	F	U	V	O	W	N	C	R	J
Q	Y	N	J	D	P	G	E	F	D	M
E	L	D	A	A	S	H	I	M	U	R

Discovery Fact™

These super-smelly planets are thought to have deadly liquid gas oceans and huge lightning storms.

Rude Robots!

Today, you can get toy robots to keep you company that behave like humans. "Robosapien" (below) can mirror even the most disgusting human functions. Read clockwise around the squares, starting from any letter, to find what two of these are.

Ⓐ

R	T
A	I
F	G N

Ⓑ

C	H I
L	N
E	B G

Answer: A. Farting, B. Belching

Bedroom Goo!

When you wake up in the morning, do you get crusty, yellow goo in the corner of your eyes? This is because your eyes constantly produce a watery substance to clean themselves. When you sleep, this liquid seeps to the corner of your eyes. Read clockwise around the squares, starting from any letter, to find out what else is in this goo.

A
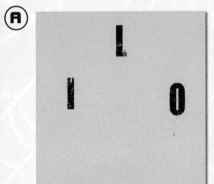

L
I O

_ _ _

B

O T E
R I
P N

_ _ _ _ _ _ _

C
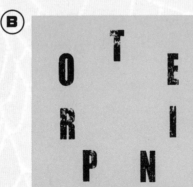

M
S U
U C

_ _ _ _ _

House of Horrors

Bathroom Terror!

Imagine sitting on the toilet and suddenly hearing a hiss! The toilet makes a cozy place for snakes to hide. This is most common in what country? Read around the word circle to find out! The first letter of the word is the letter in the center of the circle.

R A L I A U S T R A L I A

_ _ _ _ _ _ _ _ _

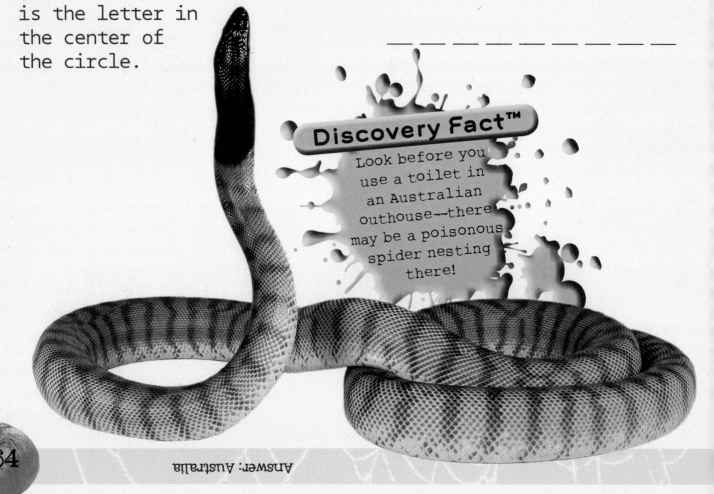

Discovery Fact™

Look before you use a toilet in an Australian outhouse—there may be a poisonous spider nesting there!

64

Monkeying Around!

The Kenyan president's house was once invaded by monkeys who smelled the delicious cooking! Work your way through the maze to find out how many monkeys there were! When you find the exit route, it will lead you to the correct answer.

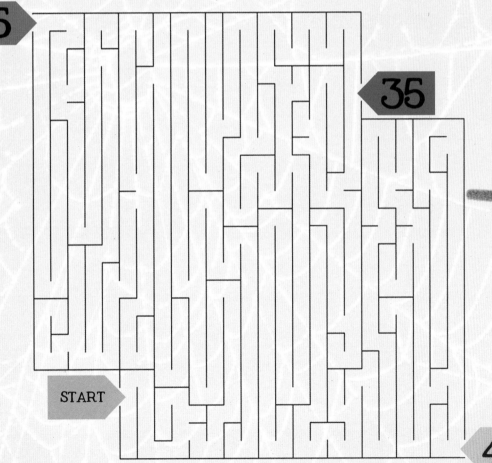

15

35

START

45

Answer: 35

Disgusting Mites!

You drop skin flakes all the time, which is good news for the millions of miniscule dust mites living in your house, because they feed on skin flakes. To them, you're like a giant, walking cookie, dropping tasty crumbs as you go by! Solve the numbers and find out how big the average dust mite is!

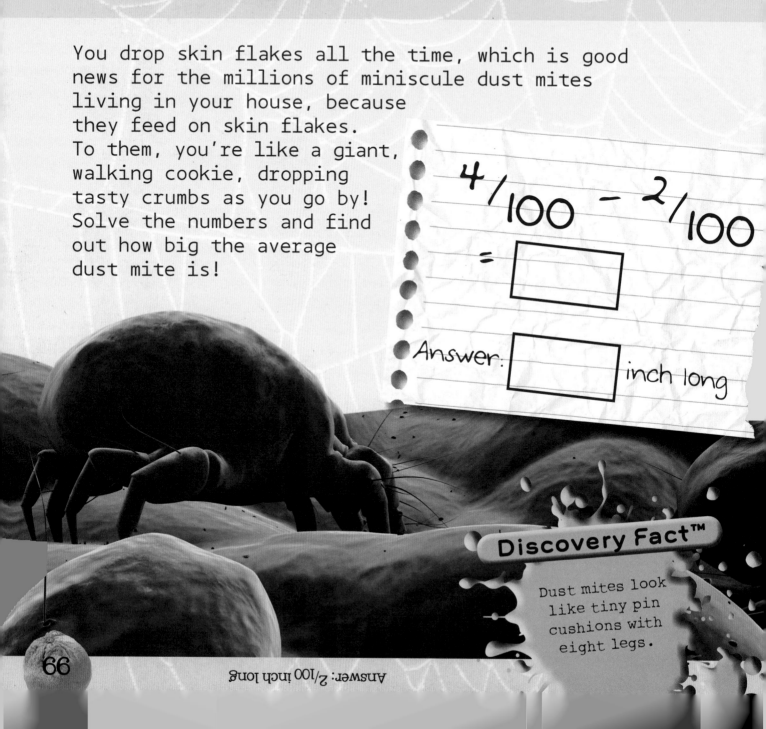

$$4/100 - 2/100$$

$$= \boxed{}$$

Answer: $\boxed{}$ inch long

Discovery Fact™

Dust mites look like tiny pin cushions with eight legs.

Answer: 2/100 inch long

Stinky Machine!

The amount of skin flakes you drop each day is enough to feed at least a million dust mites.

A full vacuum cleaner bag has a distinct smell all of its own. Unscramble the letters below to find out what makes the smell.

STUD TIMES

A ___ ___ ___ ___

EMIT OPOP

B ___ ___ ___ ___

Answer: A. Dust mites, B. Mite poop

Gross Mites!

Who would have thought such tiny creatures would have such a big yuck factor! Dust mites live for about only one month, but during that time they make an enormous amount of poop! Crack the code to find out just how much.

z	y	x	w	v	u	t	s	r	q	p	o	n	m	l	k	j	i	h	g	f	e	d	c	b	a
a	b	c	d	e	f	g	h	i	j	k	l	m	n	o	p	q	r	s	t	u	v	w	x	y	z

			g	r	n	v	h		g	s	v	r	i		l	d	m		y	l	w	b
2	0	0																				

d	v	r	t	s	g		r	m		k	l	l	k

Dust mites don't like high temperatures, so make sure you wash bedsheets at 140°F or more to kill them. Sunlight kills them, too.

Answer: 200 times their own body weight in poop.

Eerie Earwigs!

Earwigs come out at night to munch on insects and insect eggs. They also have one other favorite snack. Read clockwise around the square, starting from any letter, to find out what it is.

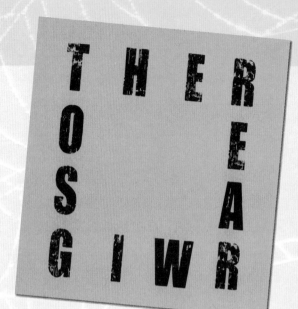

T H E R
T   E
O   R
S   A
G I W R

_____

_____ ____

Scary Centipede!

It may not look scary to us, but to other small creatures a centipede is fearsome! It can run really fast on its 15 pairs of legs, even up walls and upside down on ceilings! It kills its prey by injecting venom with its fangs—it can nip humans, too, but does not harm them. Solve the numbers to find out how big this mini beast is!

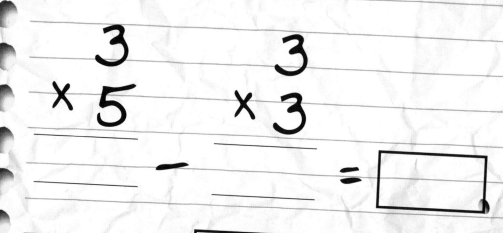

$$\begin{matrix} 3 \\ \times\ 5 \\ \hline \end{matrix} \qquad \begin{matrix} 3 \\ \times\ 3 \\ \hline \end{matrix}$$

$$\boxed{} - \boxed{} = \boxed{}$$

Answer: up to $\boxed{}$ inches long

Discovery Fact™

Centipedes roam the house looking for spiders, bedbugs, ants, cockroaches, and silverfish.

Answer: Up to 6 inches long.

Crazy Pet!

The St. Helena earwig can grow up to 3 inches long—that's as long as your index finger.

In Japan, people keep centipedes as pets. Work your way through the maze to find out what they're called. When you find the exit, it will lead you to the correct answer.

START

Gege

Gigi

Gejigeji

Answer: Gejigeji

Crane Fly!

Adult crane flies rarely feed, but their larvae eat and can seriously damage grass and crops. Crack the code to find out the name of the crane fly's larvae.

z	y	x	w	v	u	t	s	r	q	p	o	n	m	l	k	j	i	h	g	f	e	d	c	b	a
a	b	c	d	e	f	g	h	i	j	k	l	m	n	o	p	q	r	s	t	u	v	w	x	y	z

o	v	z	g	s	v	i		q	z	x	p	v	g

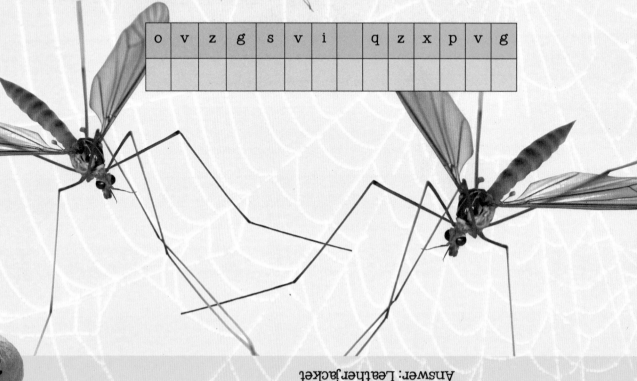

72

Bathroom Slime!

Your bathroom is a warm, wet paradise for bacteria—millions of them share your bathroom. What is the bathroom slime made by bacteria called? Solve the word circle to find out. The first letter of the word is the letter in the center of the circle.

F I L O B M I

___ ___ ___ ___ ___ ___ ___ ___

Don't Let the Bedbugs Bite!

What sort of party do bedbugs hate?
Unscramble the letters to find out.

Clue: Bedbugs don't like biting through clothes.

jpamaas

_____ _____ _____ _____ _____

Bedbug Hell!

Bedbugs live all around the world, with the exception of one habitat, where it is too cold and dry for them. Unscramble the letters to discover where this is.

staminuon

___ ___ ___ ___ ___ ___ ___ ___ ___

Midnight Snack!

Bedbugs have skin-piercing mouthparts. Can you guess what they eat? Crack the code to find their favorite food.

___ ___ ___ ___ ___

a	b	c	d	e	f	g	h	i	j	k	l	m	n

o	p	q	r	s	t	u	v	w	x	y	z

Fight Back!

There's one thing you can use to get rid of those pesky bedbugs. Read clockwise around the square, starting from any letter, to find out the answer.

L E A N E
C   R
M   V
U   A
U U C A

___ ___ ___ ___ ___ ___ ___

___ ___ ___ ___ ___ ___

Quick Fish!

This insect has three bristly tails and eats anything starchy, such as paper, cereal, books, and wallpaper. Find out what it is called, by searching the word puzzle for SILVERFISH and BLUEFISH. Whichever word comes up the most is the answer.

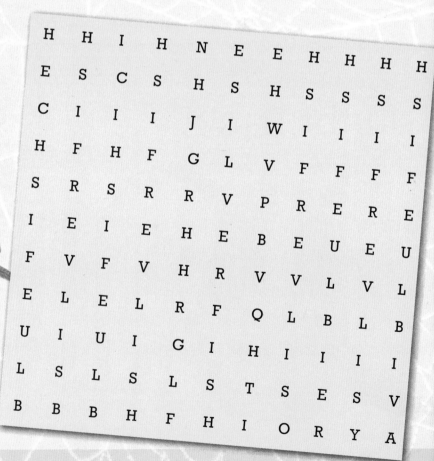

H H I H N E E H H H
E S C S H S H S S S
C I I I J I W I I I
H F H F G L V F F F
S R S R R V P R E R E
I E I E H E B E U E U
F V F V H R V V L V L
E L E L R F Q L B L B
U I U I G I H I I I I
L S L S L S T S E S V
B B B H F H I O R Y A

76

Home Sweet Home!

Here's a list of mini beasts that would find parts of your house delicious! Follow the lines to find out where each beast lives!

a. furniture beetle

b. deathwatch beetle

c. powderpest beetle

d. book louse

1. Feeds on musty old books. The glue in the spine is a special treat. The creature called a bookworm doesn't actually eat books. It eats crops, such as cotton and tobacco plants.

2. Eats wood and then poops it out as little piles of dust.

3. Will tunnel through wood and paper. Won't harm you unless you are reading this book while wearing a wooden leg.

4. Eats wood. If you hear a weird ticking noise at night, it could be this beetle trying to attract a mate (or it could be your alarm clock).

Crunchy Cockroaches!

Discovery Fact™

Cockroaches sometimes climb onto men when they're asleep and drink water off their moustaches!

Where do cockroaches most like to live in the house? Work your way through the maze below to find out! When you find the exit route, it will lead you to the correct answer.

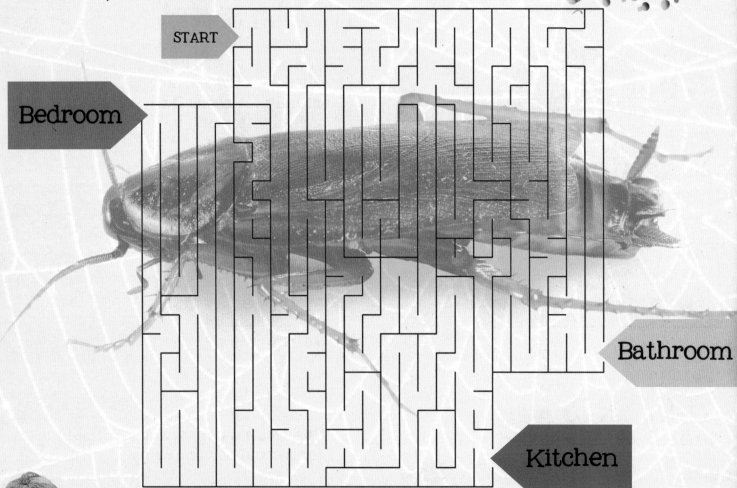

START

Bedroom

Bathroom

Kitchen

78

Runny Roaches!

You can sometimes spot where a cockroach has been, because they leave something behind them. Unscramble the letters to find out!

DISK RAKMS

_____ _____

How Many?!

There are about 30 species of cockroach that share our homes. But there are a lot more species in the world. Can you guess how many? Solve the numbers to find out.

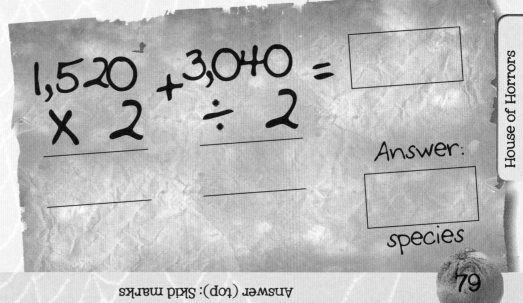

$1,520 \times 2 + 3,040 \div 2 =$

Answer:

species

Kitchen Beetles!

All kinds of horrible beetles hang out in kitchens. Search the word puzzle below for four types of food you might find them in.

Discovery Fact™

People in contact with flour mites get a skin rash called "baker's itch."

```
O K D F Y G R A I N W
N W I S W T U P F H D
N A B J Z E Q S M S O
Y B C N F I L X E O W
M P V O P K Z X H T A
B E C C O Z M B R C
R T Z A P O M J S N F
F U T B M C C Q M F S
H P O T D D W E T V I
T H B L S J O H X L M
D X U S F M B O V W G
```

Awful Aztecs!

The Mexican Aztecs invented chocolate, but they ate some really disgusting stuff, too. Read clockwise around the squares, starting from any letter, to find out what they ate.

Ⓒ

O R

W S M

Ⓐ

G R A S

S H

G S S O

R E P P O

Ⓑ

L A

E R V

A V

Ⓓ

S

T A

N

Answer: A. Grasshoppers, B. Larvae, C. Worms, D. Ants

Poop!

Some of our poop is used to fertilize farm crops. Then we eat the crops, and poop them back out ready for fertilizer to be made again! What a disgusting food cycle! Solve the word circle below to find out what human fertilizer is called. The first letter of the word is the letter in the center of the circle.

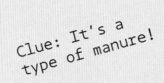

Clue: It's a type of manure!

_ _ _ _ _ _ _ _ _

Answer: Humanure

Spit Secrets!

How much spit do you think you make every day? Dribble your way through the maze to find out. When you find the exit route, it will lead you to the correct answer!

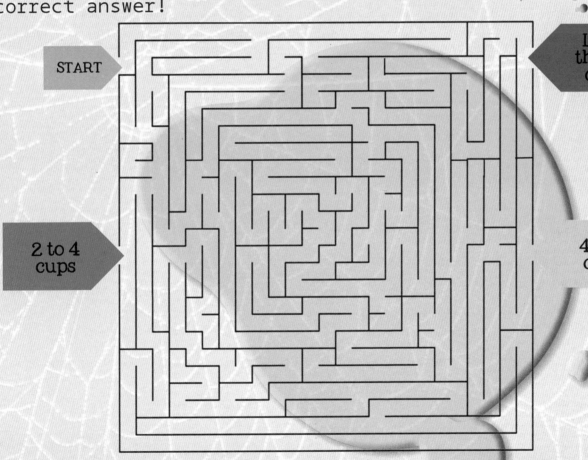

START

Less than 1 cup

2 to 4 cups

4 to 8 cups

Plague Cures!

During the Black Death (a deadly disease that swept Europe in the 1300s), people ate some very weird things hoping to be cured. Unscramble the letters to discover one "cure."

DWEPOERD   ERPLSA

_ _ _ _ _ _ _ _ _   _ _ _ _ _ _

Food from Both Ends!

Search the word puzzle to the right to discover two commonly eaten foods that come from either end of an animal.

```
T  Y  Z  Z  K  B
E  I  I  A  Z  I
X  V  L  Y  J  T
L  E  G  G  S  L
E  U  G  N  O  T
X  U  V  V  G  P
```

Fishy Fruit!

The world's smelliest fruit has to be the durian, a spiky fruit that is said to smell like rotting fish. It's banned from airplanes and trains because of its foul stink. Crack the code and find out what part of the world this stinky fruit grows in.

__ __ __ __ __ __ __   __ __ __ __

a	b	c	d	e	f	g	h	i	j	k	l	m	n

o	p	q	r	s	t	u	v	w	x	y	z

Answer: Southeast Asia

Freaky Food

Grubs Are Good!

Insects are full of protein and in many countries people snack on them! Follow the lines to find out what the favorites are in these countries.

A. Nigeria

B. Australia

C. Japan

1. **WITCHETY GRUBS, A WHITE MOTH LARVAE AS BIG AS A FINGER**

2. **BOILED WASP LARVAE**

3. **POWDERED CATERPILLAR**

Answer: A3, B1, C2.

Boogers for Dinner!

Discovery Fact™

In Lesotho, South Africa, mothers keep their babies' noses clean by sucking out the snot.

Some people eat their boogers. Do you know what the scientific name for picking your nose is? Pick your way around this maze to find out! When you find the exit route, it will lead you to the correct answer!

START

yandontpicurnose

Bogipicilicious

Rhinotillexomania

Answer: Rhinotillexomania

Freaky Food

Burp Away!

Eating contests are popular around the world, with big money prizes. Here are a few incredible eating records. Follow the lines to discover which is which!

A. Chicken nuggets

B. Hard-boiled eggs

C. Cheese sandwiches

D. Burgers

E. Waffles

F. Cow brains

1. 26 in 10 minutes

2. 29 in 10 minutes

3. 57 in 15 minutes

4. 80 in 5 minutes

5. 103 in 8 minutes

6. 65 in 6 minutes 40 seconds

Answer: A4, B6, C1, D5, E2, F3

A Lot of Gas!

Some foods you eat can make you gassy. The gas gets trapped inside you for a while until you burp or fart it out. A stomach full of gas begins to swell up, or "bloat," like a balloon. Which foods are well known for making you bloat? Unscramble the letters to find out.

A. DSOA OPP

_ _ _ _   _ _ _

B. NEABS

_ _ _ _ _

Burp On...

Here are some bubbly facts about stomach gas. Pick out which facts are true!

Sheep can suffer from **bloat** if they eat the wrong type of grass. They blow up like **balloons** and can even die.

Babies find it hard to get rid of **gas** and need help burping. Patting a baby on the back helps the **burps** to come out.

Burps will usually smell of the **food** in your stomach.

In some countries, it's polite to **burp** after a meal. People think it shows you **enjoyed** the food.

Stinky Meat!

Some meat is thought to be best served rotting. Gross! Sometimes a chef will wait until something appears on the meat before cooking it. Unscramble the letters to find out what it is.

SGOMAGT

_ _ _ _ _ _ _

Answer (bottom): Maggots

Answer (top): They are all true!

Bombay What?

Bombay duck is an Indian food famous for its silly name and its stink. However, this food isn't a duck. What is it? Read clockwise around the square, starting from any letter, to find out!

___ ___ ___ ___ ___   ___ ___ ___ ___

Smelly Cheese!

A computer with an electronic nose has officially identifed the smelliest cheese in the world. What country did it come from? Read clockwise around the square, starting from any letter, to find out!

Some types of cheese are meant to be moldy!

___ ___ ___ ___ ___ ___

Cider Cocktail!

In the past, cider makers added meat to their apple and water mixture. As the meat rotted, it helped the mixture turn into cider. What went into the vat— rats or chickens? Search the word puzzle below for RATS and CHICKENS. Whichever word comes up the most is the answer!

Discovery Fact™

Casu marzu, a maggoty cheese, is officially banned in Italy because it can make people ill.

```
Q I K I E R E U H C Y
Z L A C H I C K E N S
R C H I C K E N S X N
C A C K O W G C C R S
W L T H O T H W H G H
C W A S I I U J I N R
R A T S C C D U C F A
X F Y K G R K V K O T
M O E E S A S E E F S
J N N O K T L Z N R U
S G M W A S K I S S Z
S G B R I J J W T X E C
```

Answer: Rats

Eat Your Vegetables!

Fruit and vegetables contain vitamins we need. In the past, sailors died because they didn't eat enough fruit and vegetables. What was the disease called? Work through the maze to find out. When you find the exit route, it will lead you to the correct answer!

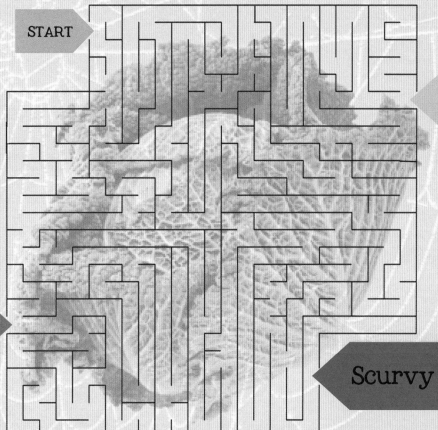

START

Flu

Chicken pox

Scurvy

Answer: Scurvy

The Right Stuff!

Sailors got sick eating polar bears' or seals' livers—both are so full of vitamin A they are poisonous.

You have to make sure you get a balanced diet, otherwise gross and horrible things can start happening to your body. Follow the lines below to find out what missing out a food group can do!

A. Milk and fish contain calcium.

B. Meat, vegetables, and fruit contain iron.

C. Meat, eggs, cheese, and nuts contain protein.

D. Milk, eggs, fruit, and vegetables contain vitamins.

1. If you don't eat this, your muscles will waste away.

2. If you don't eat this, you will get serious eye problems.

3. If you don't eat this, your bones will grow crookedly.

4. If you don't eat this, you will not have healthy blood.

Answer: A3, B4, C1, D2.

Inside Info!

What is a name for the organs of a fowl, such as the heart, liver, and gizzards sometimes used to make gravy? Work your way through this maze to find out. When you find the exit route, it will lead to you the correct answer!

Organ meats are used in traditional food, such as the Scottish haggis.

START

Figs

Giblets

Grub

Freaky Food

Answer: Giblets

Acknowledgments

Front cover: tr GK Hart/Vikki Hart/Getty, cr Thomas J Peterson/Getty, c Jason Edwards/Getty, bc Martin Harvey/Getty

1 Dreamstime.com/Marek Cosmal, 2 t Dreamstime.com/Stoupa, 2 c Dreamstime.com/Kati Neudert, 2-3 David Burder/Getty, 3 tr Gregory F Maxwell/GNU, 3 br Dreamstime.com/Paul Fleet, 4 Dreamstime.com/Stefan Ataman, 5 Dreamstime.com/Anthony Aneese Totah Jr, 7 Rigaud, 8 LemonCrumpet/Sharealike, 10 t Dreamstime.com/Szefei, 10 br LonghH/istockphoto, 11 Tommounsey/istockphoto, 12tr Dave Dunford, 12 bl Dreamstime.com/Patti Gray, 13 Bettman/Corbis, 15 Floortje/istockphoto, 16 dra_schwartz/istockphoto.com, 17 Ales Veluscek/istockphoto, 18 Christopher Kennedy/GNU, 19 Lebanmax/Dreamstime.com, 20 Dreamstime.com/Andrei Calangiu, 21 Dreamstime.com/Roger Whiteaway, 22 Dreamstime.com/Mairead Neal, 23 Dreamstime.com/Paul Fleet, 24 Dreamstime.com/Michael Thompson, 25 Dreamstime.com/Alex Gorodnitchev, 26 Dreamstime.com/Rui Gomes, 27 Dreamstime.com/Eric Isselee, 28 photomino/istockphoto.com, 29 Dreamstime.com/Aleksandr Bondarchiuk, 30 David Burder/Getty, 31 Judy Dillon/istockphoto.com, 32 b Dreamstime.com/Marek Cosmal, 32 t Dreamstime.com/Michael Lynch, 33 Dreamstime.com/Martin Krause, 34 Simon Podgorsek/istockphoto.com, 35 Dreamstime.com/Sergey Bondarenko, 36 Dreamstime.com/Niko Fagerstrom, 37 tr Dreamstime.com/Bernard Breton, 37 br Marc Dietrich/istockphoto, 38 Dennis M. Sabangan/epa/Corbis, 39 narvikk/istockphoto.com, 40 Dreamstime.com/Stanislav Komogorov, 41 Rob Bouwman/istockphoto, 42 Dreamstime.com/Stoupa, 44 b Dreamstime.com/Stoupa, 44 bl istockphoto, 45 AFP/Getty, 47 Mkartal/Dreamstime.com, 48 Katseyephoto/istockphoto.com, 49 Isselee/Dreamstime.com, 50 t Siotmoc66/Dreamstime.com, 50 b Bob Thomas/Popperfoto/Getty, 51 Rob Coxx/istockphoto.com, 52 saluha/istockphoto, 53 Warwick Lister-Kaye/istockphoto.com, 54 t Outdoorsman/Dreamstime.com, c F2/Dreamstime.com, b Naturediver/Dreamstime.com, 55 Dreamstime.com/Paige Foster, 56 LOUOATES/istockphoto, 57 Dreamstime.com/Jose Fuente, 58 Routlaw/Dreamstime.com, 59 Dreamstime.com/Anthony Hathaway, 60 NASA, 61 NASA, 62 Gene Blevins/LA Daily News/Corbis, 63 c Gregory F Maxwell/GNU, 63 t Dreamstime.com/Marzanna Syncerz, 64 Shannon Plummer/istockphoto.com, 65 Isselee/Dreamstime.com, 66 Dreamstime.com/Sebastian Kaulitzki, 67 Galdzer/Dreamstime.com, 68 Dreamstime.com/Janehb, 69 Fir0002/Flagstaffotos/GNU, 70 Cammeraydave/Dreamstime.com, 72 jamesbenet/istockphoto.com, 74 Lucabertolli/Dreamtime.com, 75 Galdzer/Dreamstime.com, 76 Dreamstime.com/Hoger Leyrer, 77 Rikko/Dreamstime.com, 78 arlindo71/istockphoto, 80 YinYang/istockphoto.com, 81 Niilo Tippler/istockphoto, 82 wsfurlan/istockphoto, 83 Sharon Dominick/istockphoto, 84 vladislav mitic/istockphoto.com, 85 Shariffic/istockphoto, 86 Dreamstime.com/Nico Smit, 87 l Dreamstime.com/Kati Neudert, 87 r Dreamstime.com/Stephen Coburn, 88 Dreamstime.com/Kati Neudert, 89 Barbro Bergfeldt/istockphoto.com, 90 Andrew Howe/istockphoto, 91 t Dreamstime.com/Alicet, 91 b Juanmonino/istockphoto.com, 92 Dreamstime.com/Oleg Kozlov, 93 egal/istockphoto.com, 94 egal/istockphoto.com, 95 Dreamstime.com/Patrick Swan